FROM THE Fields TO THE Future

7 Secrets to Living Longer from a Super-Centenarian

WRITTEN BY JOYCE ROBINSON

Library and Archives Canada Cataloguing in Publication

Robinson, Joyce, author
From the fields to the future : 7 secrets to living longer from a super-centenarian / written by Joyce Robinson.

ISBN 978-0-9812114-4-2 (pbk.)

1. Vaught, Odrick. 2. Centenarians—South Carolina—Biography. 3. Freedmen—South Carolina—Biography. 4. African Americans—South Carolina—Biography. I. Title.

E185.97.V39R62 2013 975.7'04092 C2013-902659-2

Excelovate

P.O. Box 34021
RPO Hollandview #7
Aurora, Ontario
L4G 0G3

I am grateful for the support and positive encouragement from family and friends, especially Jimmy Lee and Sandie Edge, Jean Vaught, Faye Weaver, Lenore Stackhouse, Wilemina, many others and you!

Special thanks to Excelovate Publishing and Claudette for sharing Uncle Odrick's story.

I am also thankful to Lacy Taylor who provided great photos of the Vaught family.

His Story

The Seed 7

Preface – "The Neck" – A brief history 8

Introduction "Uncle O" 12

The Emergence of Seven Secrets 15

1. Eat from the Creek 19
2. Walk Dem Fields 27
3. Smilin' and Noddin' for Love 37
4. Believe and Honour 47
5. Don't Worry 'Bout a Thing 55
6. Deal with It and Be Who You Is 63
7. Party Like it's 1956 71

The Harvest 77

A Letter from Uncle O
– From the Fields to the Future 81

The Germination 93

Certificate of Achievement 95

The Seed

PREFACE – "THE NECK"

A brief history

Within a mile of the busy U.S. Highway 17 at Little River, South Carolina, two separate and very distinct worlds exist. To the east is the resort area of Myrtle Beach, a land of fabulous, pristine beaches, stately palm trees, condominiums, and fine restaurants. To the west, between Waites Island and Little River's salt marshes, lies Little River Neck – the wild domain of the past with its dusty dirt roads, mighty oak trees, and in my humble opinion, some of the strongest men and women ever born.

Even though "the Neck" seems to be geographically and culturally isolated from the real world, this is where the Vaught family history began. Such as their forefathers, the folks in this quaint, secluded community lived simple, uncomplicated lives. People in Little River Neck made a decent living fishing and gathering clams and oysters from the nearby salt water creeks. They also farmed and hunted wild game in the oak and pine woodlands. Their healthy living was a direct result of their respect for the land and the rich waters that surrounded them on every side. Because of their unsophisticated lifestyles, many have been quite fortunate to enjoy long lives, as evidenced by Katie (Bellamy) Randall (101), Guther Bellamy (102), Lula Vaught (104), and Odrick Vaught (123).

Odrick had seen so much with his cataract-riddled eyes; he was like a rugged oak tree, his hands gnarled and twisted like the roots of the swamp cypress. His countenance shrank with age, and his skin wrinkled, watching the hypnotic sands of time course their dreary way through unrelenting winters and unforgiving summers. Such as his parents were, he was the property of Peter Vaught, a wealthy man who owned a great many slaves and nearly 5,000 acres of land.

VAUGHT PLANTATION

Horry County, South Carolina

Location: Sea shore, just north of Singleton Swash, All Saint's Parish

Number of acres: approx. 4,628 acres.

Plantation Assets: Cattle, sheep, swine, cotton, Indian corn, salt works.

Owners: Peter Vaught, Sr., Peter Vaught, Jr., William Hampton Vaught.

Slaves: As of 1864, the Vaughts owned 75 slaves.

Burroughs & Chapin Center for Marine & Wetland Studies, 2008.

Peter Vaught Sr. & Peter Vaught Jr.
Vaught Plantation Owners.

INTRODUCTION
"Uncle O"

If you are like me, you want to be healthy and you want to live a long and fulfilling life.

For years, I read books and magazines, hoping to find "the answer" to longevity. There was no shortage of opinions. The authors seemed very knowledgeable about what to eat, when to exercise and how to live.

After searching high and low for the secret, I found a group of experts with exceptional credibility and a track record for success. These experts are few and far apart – they are affectionately referred to as super-centenarians.

Super-centenarians are people who have lived past their 110th birthday. With over 40,000 days on this earth, a super-centenarian is living proof that longevity is possible. So now that you know who they are, the next challenge is to find one. My research uncovered less than 100 individuals who have been confirmed as super-centenarians … in the world!

It was a very pleasant surprise to learn that I had a relatively famous super-centenarian in my very own family. In 1965, my great-uncle, Odrick Vaught (aka

Uncle Odry) was considered by many to be the oldest man in the United States. We affectionately called him "Uncle O" and while I certainly knew he was old, I never thought of him as being one of the oldest people in the world.

After countless conversations with family members, years of researching archives and the ultimate find – locating a collection of Uncle O's photographs – it was time.

It was time to share the story of how a man born into slavery lived a long, happy and fulfilled life. A life filled with trials, adversities, remarkable joy and seven magical secrets to help us all thrive.

Odrick Vaught, legendary super-centenarian.

The Emergence of Seven Secrets

Who hasn't heard of Lucky Number Seven? The number seven is viewed as lucky in many cultures. Some folks attribute it to the Bible and the fact that it took God seven days to create the world. Others believe the number seven became lucky in ancient times because when humans looked up to the sky, they saw 7 "things," the sun, the moon and five planets.

Whether the seven dwarfs, seven seas, seven sins or the seventh son, it is widely accepted that the number 7 is a big deal, culturally, historically and scientifically.

The number seven was also of great significance to Uncle O. It was his belief that the secret to his longevity was the result of seven disciplines. These seven disciplines or Seven Secrets were not based on scientific research or a doctor's prescription. His recipe was four parts necessity, two parts experience and one part resilience.

Make no mistake, by traditional standards, Uncle O was not a sophisticated man. According to one newspaper article, he was described as the "old Negro, dressed in dirty grey britches with a tan sport coat and a grey hat." While he was not a distinguished scholar, he certainly had a lot to teach us as one of the few individuals who successfully cracked the code to longevity.

So what are the seven secrets? I thought you'd never ask. Here they are, over 110 years of experience woven into seven principles, in Odrick's own words and authentic dialect:

1. **Eat from the Creek;**
2. **Walk dem Fields;**
3. **Smilin' and Noddin' for Love;**
4. **Believe and Honour;**
5. **Don't Worry Bout' a Thing;**
6. **Be Who You Is;**
7. **Party like it's 1956.**

These seven simple secrets came from a man of very simple means. As we busy ourselves with a much faster paced life than Odrick ever knew, we should pause to find out how a man who once appeared to have nothing was able to achieve the three things many of us desire – recognition, happiness and health.

1

Eat from the Creek

On June 5, 1965, Bob Talbert wrote an article entitled, "The 120-Year Old Man". He stated, "Old men with mahogany skin and young boys with bronze-red burns gather in front of the general store and talk of super catches and sailing ketches. They also talk of Odrick Vaught. "Odrick Vaught? Sure, I know Odrick Vaught. He's nigh onto 120 years old. He's an old darkie living up yonder at Little River Neck. He's still right spry. Sure I know Odrick Vaught. Everybody does. Oldest man 'round these parts."

Uncle O lived in a small community with his unusually large family and it was normal to see tens of children running around. He was accustomed to dusty dirt roads, moss-dripping oaks, the warm climate and a simple, unencumbered life.

As the sun rose early in the morning, Uncle Odrick followed suit. He would walk down the winding, sand-rutted road to the creek less than a mile behind his house. He knew the marshy creek, studded with tall sawgrass well. Of course he did, he fished in them and gathered oysters and clams.

The questions he was most-frequently asked were also the questions he was always happy to answer: "How are you living so long? What is your secret?" He never missed a beat and firmly believed the most significant reason was his habit of eating raw oysters from the salt water creek.

His wife, Hattie, also quoted in the Talbert article, "All his life, he done nothing but farm and fish and raise likker and children. Today, Odrick Vaught eats "only what comes outten the crik".

Vaught's doctor, N.F. Nixon of Cherry Grove, said he had been trying to get Hattie to bring her husband in for a physical examination with little success. "The fact that he has lived out of the creek for all those years may tell us something. He was eating full organisms and this could contribute to his long life."

According to a *Sun News* journalist in the article "Wish We Could Get Some Lights", Hattie pictured next to Odrick said, Uncle Odry was born down at Long Bay where his mother was a slave. During her life, he's worked in the creek more than anywhere else. "That's what he says has helped him to live so long, eating oysters and clams," Hattie said, laughing.

Three years later, Eldridge Thompson wrote an article in the *State Newspaper*, Columbia, South Carolina on February 10, 1968 (No One Knew Lincoln When Odrick Vaught Was Born) and in the *Sun News*, February 15, 1968 (Man Who Recalls Lincoln's Assassination Gravely Ill). It was stated, "Vaught who no doubt is the nation's oldest Medicare patient, has "eaten out of the creek" all his life. Oysters, shrimp and fish have been his diet throughout his 123-years of life in Horry County."

Did Uncle Odry get this one right? Are there magical properties in the creek that give our bodies more strength and our days more length?

A quick stroll down research lane appears to suggest that eating 1 to 2 servings of fish each week can reduce a host of diseases found in children and adults. As a low fat, high protein offering rich in omega 3 fatty acids, people who regularly choose fish will be armed with better weapons when battling ailments such as depression, dementia, heart disease and some forms of cancer.

A 2006 Harvard School of Public Health study identified a key finding related to fish and our overall health. The comprehensive study revealed that the benefits of eating fish outweigh any perceived risks. Moreover, the consumption of fish and fish oils can reduce total mortality by 17%. This certainly lends credence to Uncle

Odrick's number one secret – stop wasting your time at the restaurants, take out your fishing rod and head for the creek.

Okay
By
Uncle O

Take Action

Shellfish and crustaceans are great sources of low fat protein. The following six fish varieties are healthy options for everyone (including children and pregnant women).

Replace your regular dinner menu twice a week with some delicious seafood and enjoy your big step down longevity lane.

- **Flounder**
- **Oysters**
- **Trout**
- **Scallops**
- **Shrimp**
- **Cod**

Give a man a fish and you feed him
for a day;
teach a man to fish and you feed him
for a lifetime.

ANNE RITCHIE

Oliver Edge — Uncle Odrick's close friend.

Susan Bellamy (family friend) and Lula Vaught Randall
(Uncle Odrick's Niece), clamming in the Creek.

Top photo: Local shop owner Mr. Dalton admires the 'Catch of the Day.'

Bottom photo: Uncle O was of great interest to many. Here we see Professor Glenn Smith, writer (left) interviewing neighbor Mosses Moss (right).

2

2 Walk Dem Fields

Uncle Odrick did a lot of walking in his lifetime. He walked everywhere. Throughout the week he walked down the dirt road, about a half mile to the creek to fish and gather clams and oysters.

He walked to church on Sundays and to special events held at the Macedonia AME Church, approximately a quarter of a mile from his home. It was a regular occurrence to see Uncle O walking 4 miles to go to and from the grocery store at Nixon's Crossroads. Odrick never cared to own an automobile or learn bout drivin', he enjoyed walking. That was his way of getting what he referred to as "plenty exercise" and how he kept his body active and physically fit. The second secret to his longevity was movement and rest. Uncle O let his body tell him when enough was enough, and after every long walk, he also enjoyed his fair bit of rest.

Allegedly Uncle O lived from the beginning to the end of the Civil War, saw World War I and World War

II fought and won, lived through the escalation of the Vietnam War, lived through 26 of the 43 Presidents of the United States (from James K. Polk to Lyndon B. Johnson, including Grover Cleveland, who served two non-consecutive terms), and was alive when 24 of the states gained statehood. He lived through so much in his lifetime – he witnessed advancements in manufacturing, technology and science – yet he preferred using the same mode of transport he used back in the fields: walking.

Exercise and relaxation seem like simple concepts. You may be asking what's the big secret here. The secret is not knowing what you should do, it's all in the doing. Whatever your lot in life, some things are the same for all of us. We all have a heart, we all have one life and we all have the same amount of time in the day. Setting aside time for regular exercise and rest periods were both very important to Uncle O. The question to ask yourself is: How important is regular exercise and rest for me?

According to the Mayo Clinic, exercise may be the answer to increased energy and longevity. Their research highlighted 7 benefits to regular physical activity:

- **Weight control;**
- **Combat disease;**
- **Stress management;**
- **Boost energy;**

- **Improve rest periods;**
- **Enhanced love life;**
- **Opportunities to strengthen relationships AND have fun.**

The physical and mental benefits of increased activity are astounding. In this day and age, a common concern for young people and adults is stress. Exercising reduces stress hormones such as cortisol and adrenaline, while bringing positive changes to the body and spirit.

Did you know that exercise also plays a key role in protecting us from colds and flu by elevating our immunoglobulin levels? Immuno what? Perhaps you've heard of an antibody. The words antibody and immunoglobulin are used interchangeably and in the most simplistic sense, they are proteins in our bodies used by our immune systems to find and destroy bacteria and viruses.

In researching longevity, I read about an interesting study completed at a Canadian university where it was discovered that exercise reduced or eradicated almost every harmful aging effect in mice. The ground-breaking study by Dr. Mark Tarnopolsky led him to the irrefutable conclusion that "Exercise alters the course of aging and anything is better than nothing".

While your dream of beating Superstar Jamaican Sprinter Usain Bolt in a 100 Meter race may never come true, consider what a little movement could mean for your health and wellness.

This brings us to the other end of the spectrum. If you'll remember, Uncle O's secret was exercise and relaxation. You can't be go-go-go all the time. In this hyper-connected world we live in, words like downtime, rest and relaxation are sometimes frowned upon.

In 2006, a Harvard survey revealed that people were sleeping less than six hours a night. Corporations celebrate the high-performing executives willing to work 16 hour days, blaze through emails overnight and hit the social scene in the evening to keep the clients nice and happy.

Exactly when did sleep become something for the weak and downwardly-mobile?

Uncle O was certainly onto something special here. Countless studies have proven that rest and sleep are vital to our longevity. One interesting study in the 1980's kept rats awake for what was described as "indefinitely". So, how long is indefinitely? They began dying after five days of enforced lack of sleep. Subsequent studies have proven that while the duration of rest differs from species to species, the one thing that unifies us is that we all need some form of rest to survive.

The value of rest is very powerful and a few of the notable benefits include:

- **Better learning and memory;**
- **Enhanced creativity and problem solving;**
- **Improved metabolism, physical conditioning and moods.**

This Uncle O secret is really about balance. It's about finding the time to move more, and surprisingly, setting aside at least 7-10 hours a day to relax and move less.

Okay By Uncle O

Take Action

Making a big change requires a big commitment. For some of us, the bigger the commitment, the tougher the challenge and regrettably, the easier it is to fail. Take Uncle Odrick's 24/7 challenge and build your strength and resolve over time. This challenge requires you to start small by committing to:

- **Exercise for 24 minutes each day;**
- **Sleep for 7 hours each night.**

Whether you are strolling down a dirt road like Uncle O, riding your bike or doing serious damage on an elliptical machine, start small, do something and do it now.

"We don't need to stop exercising
because we grow old –
we grow old because we stop exercising."

DR. KENNETH COOPER

Wash Day at Uncle Odrick's and Hattie's house.

Uncle O resting after a long day.

3

3 Smilin' and Noddin' for Love

I learned a lot about Uncle O from family members, but I also found some interesting facts and quotes from a publication called "*Berry's Blue Book*". Berry's Blue Book – A Book of Historical Interviews was authored by Connelly Burgin Berry (known as Burgin). Burgin was born in North Carolina in 1919 but moved to Sand Hills of Chesterfield County, South Carolina in 1925.

Burgin interviewed people of the Carolina areas for more than fifty years and it was no surprise that one day he found himself looking into the wise old eyes of Uncle O. It is in Berry's Blue Book where secret number three is revealed, "smilin' and noddin' for love". Uncle O had two wives, 20 children to his second wife Hattie, and a very positive outlook and perspective on life. By the time Burgin visited Uncle O's modest two-room dwelling, he was happily married to his second wife, Hattie. They had no running water, lived without electricity and yet they were very happy. In Burgin's Blue Book, we get a glimpse of interviewers such as Bob Talbert from *The State* newspaper, At-large, Horry County Rep, John Jeanrette Jr, and Bill Collins for the *Sun News*, asking Uncle O probing and pointed questions. In many cases, it was his 66 year old wife Hattie cheerfully jumping in to answer question after question. Uncle O could hardly get a word in. How did he react to Hattie? We find a beautiful observation from Jeanrette Jr. who impatiently watched all of Hattie's interjections. He shared his reflection with these words, "All the time, Odrick Vaught's head nodded in agreement, his lips curled in a smile."

The love shared between Uncle O and Hattie was special. In an article written in the *Sun News*, February 15, 1968 entitled, "No One Knew Lincoln When Odrick Vaught Was Born," Eldridge Thompson wrote, "At his bedside is his second wife, Hattie, who gave birth to 20 of Uncle Odrick's children." Uncle Odrick and Hattie were married for over 50 years and remained partners and soul mates until the day he died.

When an interviewer asked Hattie about the quality of her marriage, she responded with, "Uncle Odry is a mighty good husband and he hasn't caused me much trouble."

Could the answer to longevity really be found in what

some view as the most impactful four-letter word in the English language: love?

Recent studies have found that having a life partner is good for our mental and physical health. Long-term marriages that are stable and supportive result in lower mortality rates as proved in a 2004 study from the Centers for Disease Control and Prevention. Dr. Scott Haltzman, author of *The Secrets of Happy Families: Eight Keys to Building a Lifetime of Connection and Contentment* stated that "Ninety percent of married women who were alive at age 45 make it to 65." For women who are divorced or never married, their chances of seeing their 65th birthday hovered around the eighty percent mark.

Such as their female counterparts, married men also shared the same odds, with 90% making it to 65 years of age. Unmarried or divorced men fared the worst, with only a 60% chance of achieving retirement age.

So, what's all the fuss about walking down the aisle and living in matrimonial bliss? If knowing that married folks have lowered risks of strokes, cancer and heart attacks isn't enough, you may want to consider the social element. Single life is lonely and humans are social creatures who crave relationships. Companies like Match.com, eHarmony and even Ashley Madison exist for a reason, we need comfort and companionship.

Finding love, being in love and making love gives

us energy, reduces our stress and, in many cases, drives us to being more optimistic toward life. We see things through a new and exciting lens of possibilities.

Uncle O's lens was very unique. In 1959, an interviewer described Uncle O's dwelling as "wretched squalor." Uncle O and Hattie spoke of their home as a blessing and only longed for electricity. Another interviewer commented on the "old, dirt-grey handkerchief, knotted about" Hattie's head. Some people looked at Hattie and Uncle O and felt disgust or pity. When Uncle O looked at Hattie, their two room dwelling and the life they shared, he beamed with pride. When she spoke, he couldn't help but smile and nod.

He was a man in love. Hattie was his partner, his woman and soul mate. They cared for each other and on his final day on this earth, she sat by his bedside, held his hand, and gave him comfort as she watched him die.

I think Bill Collins said it best. After spending a day with the couple, Bill Collins, writer at the *Sun News* concluded his 1965 article with this remark, "… one thing is evident, Uncle Odry has got a good wife in Hattie!"

Take Action

Okay By Uncle O

This activity is the easiest to tell and perhaps the hardest to make happen. Your mission is to find a life partner. Not just any partner, you need to find someone that makes you smile, loves you unconditionally, and as Hattie said "won't cause you too much trouble".

"Love does not dominate; it cultivates."

JOHANN WOLGANG VON GOETHE

Hattie Vaught (Uncle O's Wife) prepares a meal on the stove.

THE PROGRESS-INDEX

February 18, 1968

14 The Progress-Index, Sunday, February 18, 1968

Hospital Library Draws Compliments

Medical, Student Nurse Libraries Are Combined

Much Study Goes On In New Medical Library At Petersburg General

Mrs. Brown Checks Card File Of Periodicals

Petersburg Man To Visit Old Friend Believed 123

Skin Testing Program Set

Housewives ... Class

> At his bedside is his second wife Hattie, who gave birth to 20 of Uncle Odrick's children.

> Whatever number of children, Vaught no doubt is the nation's oldest Medicare patient.

Uncle Odrick chilling with the love of his life, Hattie.

Relationships with family and friends were important to Uncle O and Hattie. Martha Lee and Melvin Moss were close neighbors.

4

Believe and Honour

Uncle Odrick faithfully attended Macedonia AME church in Little River Neck, South Carolina. The modest church was actually a single-room wooden structure located on the north side of Little River Neck Road, approximately a quarter of a mile from Uncle O's home.

Uncle Odrick played the accordion on special occasions and attended every funeral held at the church.

In his Blue Book, C.B. Berry made a notation on September 22, 1959. After speaking with many of the Little River Neck locals about Uncle O, he wrote, "I was told that he never misses church services, usually being the first one there."

Uncle O was a believer. He held firm convictions in the existence of a higher power. His great respect for leadership was evidenced by his commitment to his church and his high regard for the many great men that presided over the United States of America. Uncle O had seen Presidents come and go but the one who had the greatest impact on him was John Fitzgerald Kennedy. For Odrick Vaught, President Kennedy gave him hope and the one thing family members recollect vividly is that Uncle O felt included. In his eyes, President Kennedy cared about everyone, including the disadvantaged and poor. For Uncle O, inclusiveness was the true sign of leadership and President Kennedy gave him something to believe in – a better future.

Are belonging and believing that important? Can going to church and political engagement really be the antidote for longer life?

A study found in the Journal of the American Board of Family Medicine revealed that going to religious services can add two to three years to your life. The act of going to church involves getting engaged, participating in a community and for many, developing a greater sense of purpose. Collectively, these factors play a significant role in your health and well-being.

In 2011, a Gallup-Healthways Well-Being Index uncovered that church goers experienced more positive emotions than their home-bound counterparts. Positive emotions included actions such as laughing and smiling. The act of going to church typically involves hearing a positive message and singing along to hymnals that reinforce goodness and virtue. Those sitting in the church pews walk away with new learning, less stress and a higher degree of happiness.

For those subscribing to the Big Bang Theory, dedicating a few hours each Sunday to review Bible scriptures may present a personal challenge. If political participation is more aligned with your belief structure, you will be pleased to know that small degrees of political engagement and actions, such as voting and volunteering can also result in lower mortality rates.

Age always seems to play a key role in politics. Younger candidates get a lot of press because we expect our political leaders to be greying at the temples, wiser and older than the masses. While there is a long-standing belief that John F. Kennedy was the youngest of the US Presidents at 43 years of age, there was one former-President who led our nation at the tender age of 42 years, 10 months and 18 days old, President Theodore Roosevelt.

Research suggests that as we become more conscious of our mortality, we tend to get more engaged in the world around us, socially and politically. This increased consciousness of our mortality is also referred to as mortality salience. The key learning here is that many individuals spend the first half of their lives focused on themselves. Based on the two studies below, we find there are many benefits in shifting our thinking from "I" to "We". . . and the earlier the better!

- **The Longitudinal Study of Aging discovered that individuals who volunteered their time had lower mortality rates than those who did not.**
- **A National Health Interview Survey found that 22% of Seniors who volunteered their time in 1983 were still alive in 1991.**

Uncle Odrick believed in God, honoured his leaders and dedicated much of his time to the community in which he lived. As many of us dream about freedom at 55 or plan for retirements that involve island-hopping and fruity drinks, remember Uncle O's active community involvement at 100 years of age. Striking the right balance between giving and getting can potentially alter the course of your life.

Take Action

Get involved in your community. Social networks can occur locally or online in the digital space. Uncle O took part in his community and that engagement enriched his life with greater social support. Your assignment is to join 2 new organizations. They could be business or personal, online or offline, religious or political. The choice is yours – add a new dimension to your world and get involved.

Okay By Uncle O

The ends you serve that are selfish
will take you no further than yourself.
The ends you serve for all, will take you
into eternity.

MARCUS GARVEY

THE ROBESONIAN

January 17, 1964

Page 9—The Robesonian, Monday, January 17, 1964

Light Of 120 Years Flashes In Eyes Of S. C. Patriarch

Great Quake, Fort Sumter, Lincoln, All In His Time

ODRICK VAUGHT, after 120 years.

All of Odry's 120 years have been lived on or near the ocean and like every other old-timer he has his own special formula for longevity.

Born to slave parents, he took the name of the plantation owner, Vaught, and was a strapping lad of 16 when the cannons boomed at Fort Sumter.

"I jest wants the world the way it was when that Mr. Kennedy was alive," he says.

The old man's wants are simple. He's not worried about painting, or sealing or fires.

ODRICK AND HATTIE with prized possession.

THE VAUGHTS have four walls, a bed and a stove.

MOSES VAUGHT, 80, son of Odrick.

Two Youths Face Larceny Charges

Deaths & Funerals

Man Convicted In Taxi Robbery

To Hold Joint Session

Ouster Of N.C. Banking Chief Viewed By Moore

Uncle Odrick and wife Hattie admire a picture of
President Kennedy and First Lady.

5

Don't Worry 'Bout a Thing

Francis Bacon was an English philosopher and essayist born in 1561. One of his famous quotes addressed materialistic behaviours; Bacon believed that "money was a great servant but a bad master."

Uncle Odry stood firmly on the direct opposite end of materialism. He was a simple man, a humble soul and a complete minimalist. Admittedly, this was more a matter of circumstance than choice but choice certainly played a role in his overall comportment. When a journalist from the *Charlotte Observer* visited Uncle O and asked him to comment on his lifestyle, he humbly stated, "I don't worry 'bout a thing."

He never owned a car but once owned an ox. He didn't long for external trappings because he experienced a degree of wealth that few have the opportunity to enjoy – a fulfilled life. There was a strong alignment between the things he wanted and the things he had.

You see, Uncle O was never lonely because he had 20 children, six living at the time of his passing, 30 grandchildren, 22 great-grandchildren and a loving wife. Uncle O didn't live in a mansion but he had a roof over his head, access to nutritious food, he engaged in his community and was able to keep active mentally and physically.

His personal story was attracting reporters from several states and even journalists from Canada, who found Uncle Odry to be an interesting and intriguing character.

While it seems easier to envy the privileged and wealthy, it is common knowledge that wealth and happiness do not always go hand in hand. Having more doesn't mean the rich are living free of problems. Conversely, having less does not guarantee a life filled with purpose and eternal happiness. The difference lies within the focus and value placed on material possessions and the lengths to which people will go in order to achieve the status or obtain the things money can buy.

If you find that your material possessions are taking over your life and now possess you, it is time for a change. How does living simply and unlearning the desire to covet possessions contribute to longer life? When we strive to keep up with the Jones' and attempt to live beyond our means, we introduce stress into our world. The two types of stress you should be aware of are Eustress and Distress.

Eustress is a more positive form of stress that assists with your development and long-term growth. It is common to experience Eustress when you have a life-changing event such as marriage or the birth of a child. Taking on a new job or assignment typically involves doing something different and unfamiliar. You may experience some stress while going through these experiences but, in most cases, they are linked to positive changes, which enable you to evolve personally or professionally.

Distress is very different and can result in harmful effects. If you feel that pressure is exerted on you from every angle for a prolonged period, it's time to make a few changes. Are you surrounding yourself with the wrong people and feeling minimal joy in your life? If so, this will invite illness and disease to set in and the impacts can be harmful. Stress has been known to adversely affect the immune and cardiovascular systems. We also tend to make bad decisions when we are experiencing chronic stress; decisions that lead to obesity, alcoholism and depression.

We've all been to a funeral and most of us have heard the phrase, "you can't take it with you." For all the material things we have, in the end, we go as we came, alone and with nothing. It's not the cars, homes, jewels or cash that keep us thriving. In their 2011 book, *The Longevity Project*, Drs. Friedman and Martin made several key findings. The one that resonated with me related to connections. They found that most people who live long lives do so as a result of "long-lasting, meaningful connections with others."

It would appear that American recording artist Jennifer Lopez (J-Lo) had it right all along as documented in her song "Jenny from the Block." Our cultural roots and quality of life are far more important than the material things we acquire. It's never too late to simplify your life.

Take Action

If you want to live longer and be happy, it doesn't get any better than this; your task is to get Glad. Glad as in "Glad Garbage Bags!" Don't wait for Spring to perform your cleaning, take action now. It's time to take a step toward detaching yourself from the material things that don't bring you joy or are of no use to you. Go through your living space and separate your things into three categories. After sorting, you must find a home for each grouping within 72 hours:

1. **THINGS TO KEEP because I use and need them.**
2. **THINGS TO GIVE AWAY OR DONATE because I don't use or need them.**
3. **THINGS TO TRASH because they don't work and are of no use to anyone.**

If you find yourself spending time stressing over material things, you are placing your energy and focus on the meaningless. There is nothing wrong with wanting nice things, just don't let them consume you. Life is too short; invest your time in people who make you smile.

As for the material stuff, don't worry 'bout a thing, you're too blessed to be stressed.

There are two ways to get rich.
Either get more, or want less.

THOR DUFFIN

THE PROGRESS-INDEX

February 23, 1968

The Progress-Index, Friday, February 23, 1968

George H. Valentine (R) Explains Savings Proposal To Spec. 5 Brian C. Barnes

Army 'Saves' $6,104, Worker Presented Top January Bonus

Area News Briefs

Pay Compliments

Tobacco Meeting

Ex-Slave Dead

Voting Delegate

Turkey

Topic Scheduled For PTO Meet

Ruritans Aid Heart Fund In Dinwiddie

Jaycees Seek Nominations For Award

Obituaries

Wilbur D. Sharpe

Clayton D. Oliver

Funeral Notice

Magazine Prints Youth's Free Verse

Dr. Sayers Addresses Local Knights

WESLEY METHODIST CHURCH

Colonial Heights, Va.

Dear Friends,

Just a few words to let you know that we're having another HYMN SING at our church next Sunday, Feb. 25 at 8 p.m. You are cordially invited to attend.

Byron S. Hallstead, Pastor

Stores lots of frozen foods ...Makes ice jet fast!

'No Frost 16' Refrigerator-Freezer

As Low As $3.25 A Week

"A Servicing Dealer"

M. W. GILL & SON, INC.

20-26 W. BANK ST. RE 2-6011

FREE ADJACENT PARKING

SHOP-RITE

COURTLAND SAUSAGE ... lb. pkg. 35c

IS THE TIME YOU NEED COMPLETE

COMFORT

DELTA OIL

The Winning Combination for Oil Heat Comfort

DIAL RE-DELTA

"Serving The Tri-City Area For Over 40 Years"

Ex-Slave Dead

PETERSBURG – A friend of James Perry Edge of Petersburg, Odrick Vaught, the ex-slave who claimed to be 123 years old, died in a Myrtle Beach, S.C., hospital during the weekend.

Edge, who had known the ex-slave since childhood went to Myrtle Beach as soon as he heard of his old friend's illness.

The old man's doctor, N. F. Nixon, said he believed he was as old as he claimed although no records were kept in South Carolina at the time he was born.

6

6 Deal with It and Be Who You Is

Ironically, when your claim to fame is living long, the day you stop breathing becomes a very newsworthy event. Uncle O's death was reported internationally and many of the headlines referred to him as a former slave, ex-slave or a man born into slavery. When C.B. Berry met with Uncle Odry in 1959, he spoke of his father being a slave belonging to Peter Vaught of Vaught. His reference to Vaught related to a former post office located between Windy Hill and Myrtle Beach.

According to family members, at some point in his life, Uncle Odrick and his first wife Frances owned 37 acres in the Myrtle Beach area. It was documented in a few articles that Uncle O also owned "one oxen." To own 37 acres in Myrtle Beach today would definitely secure Uncle O a guest spot on the Millionaire Matchmaker reality show. Unfortunately, Uncle O and Patti, the host of Millionaire Matchmaker, will never set eyes on each other for two obvious reasons. Uncle O passed away in 1968, and well before he passed away, he separated and later divorced from Frances. As per their arrangement, Frances kept the land and Uncle O relinquished his claim to the property ownership, which would eventually become millions of dollars in prime real estate.

In 1965, Uncle O and his second wife Hattie faced a new challenge when their house burned to the ground. They walked away with their lives but nothing more. All their possessions were gone – clothes, furniture, photographs and their most valuable keepsake, the Bible that served as their single database for all family records. This bible had been used to capture information related to family births, deaths and key events. In an instant, everything was gone and Uncle O took it all in stride.

When asked by one reporter to comment on his life, he responded with what the article described as a voice with a croak and a rattle:

"I is old. But I do's what the Bible tells me..." and then Odrick Vaught lapsed into a sing-song recitation of a Bible passage, "...that your days may be long... in the land thy God giveth thee..."

Uncle O was resilient. Whatever the adversity, he always seemed to bounce back. How did this man, described as a former slave, a man who left all his worldly belongings to start fresh, learn never to give up? A marital breakdown was the reason for leaving 37 acres and an ox behind to start anew. After 45 years with Hattie, he experienced a devastating setback and lost all of his possessions in the fire. One would expect him to place some focus on these tribulations when asked to reflect on his life experiences. Yet, Odrick Vaught viewed the question as an opportunity to praise God and break out into song.

Scientists studying the mind and body connection have found high degrees of optimism can significantly extend life. We've already learned that stress and depression can negatively impact physical well-being. In recent years, this is changing radically from general feel-good platitudes to being fully embraced by the scientific community. Mind–body connection research is becoming mainstream; thousands of papers are being written and hundreds of projects are being funded so we can gain a better understanding as to how the ideas and thoughts that swirl around in our heads impact the many systems that keep our bodies alive.

Two surprising ways to deal with adversity involve music and laughter. Music has long been used in healing therapies and can deliver benefits such as lowering blood pressure, relaxing tension and enhancing memory.

In 2010, a study published in the International

Journal of Psychiatry in Medicine examined the records of 53,500 individuals and found that having a sense of humour aids in keeping folks healthy, while increasing the likelihood of people getting to the retirement corridor and crossing that threshold in good condition. The study also found the benefits of having a great sense of humour began to diminish after the age of 70 and all related positive effects attributed to humour were gone by age 75.

From Uncle O, we learned that adversity is to be expected and dealt with productively. While divorce rates continue to climb in North America, chances are, you will never be forced into slavery or experience the pain of rebuilding your life after a fire that destroyed everything you've worked so hard to achieve. I can confidently assure you, your challenges will be different from those of Uncle O's, but you will be challenged.

That's when you have to decide, sink or swim; laugh or cry; suffer in silence or sing with loved ones.

We will all experience loss, yet it is how we deal with it that makes us who we are.

Take Action

Okay By Uncle O

This activity is about reflection. After every adversity, take some time to reflect on what occurred and provide a response to the following two questions:

1. **What lessons have you learned from the experience?**
2. **What will you do differently if ever faced with the same challenge?**

Record your responses on two sticky notes – one for each response – and place them where you can see them every day; in your washroom, on your fridge, in your car or at your desk.

Keep the notes up for a minimum of one year.

Your scars can become stars.

ROBERT H. SCHULLER

Uncle Odrick relaxing and living simply
– with no worries.

Top photo: Mosses Moss – Uncle Odrick's neighbor and friend.

Bottom photo: Uncle O's friends and family helped him through tough times. Shown is Sammy Vaught ***Uncle Odrick's son***, left; Mosses Moss (middle) and Richard Earl Moss, right.

7

Party Like it's 1956

In 1956, when the July 5th edition of *Jet Magazine* was published, it featured the beautiful Sally Blair on the cover with the caption, "TV gave her a shot in the arm."

The up and coming female singer was dubbed a 1954 rising star by *Hue* magazine. Ms. Blair was young, talented and living her dream.

As one leafed through the July 5th *Jet Magazine*, another rising star made his debut on page 18. If you've been paying attention, you will note the rising star was none other than Mr. Odrick Vaught, pictured alongside his 21 year old twin daughters and beloved wife Hattie. The notation below the photograph read, "Birthday Party at 110".

Make no mistake, Uncle O was all about good living but he also had a few habits some may consider a little naughty. Like many of us, he had vices that astonishingly involved smoking and drinking. As Hattie described to Horry County Rep. John Jeanrette Jr., "He still got life in him. He drinks when he kin git something. Pshaw, a half-pint ain't even a swallow to him. All his life he done nothing but farm and fish and raise likker and children. He used to drink whiskey fo' water."

As for smoking, Hattie reflected on a time when Uncle O was a heavy smoker, "Stay up all night smokin' dem pipes. Scratchin' matches and smokin'."

Now don't get too excited. This is not an endorsement for you to reach for a flask and start scratchin' matches to light up a Marlboro cigarette. Consider this a dose of reality, specifically Uncle O's reality. He was like every other human being, he was imperfect, he had vices AND he lived past his 100th birthday.

With all this drinking and smoking, perhaps the key to his longevity was simply good genes. Another consideration frequently debated was his limited access to the bad stuff. Hattie clearly stated, he only indulged whenever he could "git it," but it's not clear how often he actually got it.

History has spoken and in this case, it has uncovered that the path to longevity is not always paved with those who abstain from smoking and alcohol.

Uncle O wasn't partying like a rockstar but he certainly enjoyed his life and he liked to treat himself from time to time. Hattie made it very clear when she proudly boasted, "Yessir, he still likes a drink whenever he can git one. And it won't moonshine, it come from Wilmington!"

Even more important than what he drank at his parties was who he invited to them. Celebration was essential to Uncle O and having a good time was only possible when he was surrounded with his friends and family. He had once commented that he felt he was living on "borrowed time." Is this why he never seemed to sweat the small stuff and found delight in everything and everyone around him?

According to one report, "Uncle O never travelled far from his home in Little River Neck where he farmed small sandy fields, hunted in the oak and pine woodlands and fished the nearby marsh creeks." His world was small, he was grateful, and he celebrated his life in a simple, yet meaningful way.

Okay By Uncle O

Take Action

October 1st is the International Day for Older Persons. This is the day to celebrate a special senior in your life and the way you take action is by hosting an event for one or many seniors to show your appreciation. It could be a small home-cooked meal for two, a walk in the park, or a conversation over a glass of red wine or Perrier. Be inquisitive, ask questions, solicit their opinions, explore, learn and discover together. Let's make every October 1st a special day for your special person starting now.

The more you praise and celebrate your life,
the more there is in life to celebrate.

OPRAH WINFREY

JET MAGAZINE

July 15, 1956

Birthday Party At 110: Celebrating his 110th birthday at Cherry Grove Beach, S. C., Odrick Vaught is feted by his wife and 21-year-old twin daughters while some 33 other children, 30 grandchildren and 22 great-grandchildren helped with festivities. Vaught still walks four miles daily to grocery, fishes and does light farming.

The Harvest

Uncle Odry's life was a course in living your best with the hand you're dealt. His life wasn't easy but it was relevant, meaningful and celebrated. These 7 Secrets are powerful and the 7 Actions endorsed by Uncle Odrick are small steps to bring you a little closer to achieving a longer and richer life.

1. **Eat from the Creek;**
2. **Walk dem Fields;**
3. **Smilin' and Noddin' for Love;**
4. **Believe and Honour;**
5. **Don't Worry Bout' a Thing;**
6. **Be Who You Is;**
7. **Party like it's 1956.**

Imagine if Uncle Odry wrote a letter on his last day. After years of interviews and research, I leave the final words to Uncle O. In his many hours spent with reporters in interviews, he hid special gifts for us all. He gathered these gifts by the side of the creek and within the sandy fields he farmed for decades. The time has come for the gifts to be unwrapped and shared with the world.

Consider this a small token of appreciation from his field to your future.

Uncle O & Hattie looking fine in their hats!

Uncle O, See the wisdom and experience in the eyes of the South Carolina Patriarch.

A Letter from Uncle O — From the Fields to the Future

(compiled by J. Robinson)

Dear Future,
How ole am I? Some says hunner an four, some says hunner thirteen and others says a hunner and twinny three! One thing I know for certain... I is old — but I do's what the Bible tells me.

I dun had thangs and I lost thangs. It sho made me sad but it tawt me lessens.

Watchin' my children born and watchin' dem die. I'm still happy. It meks me happy 'cause even tho I only have six alive wen I pass'd, I watched all of dem live... and live good.

It sho felt good when all dem fancy reporters drove upto what they called my "battered, fly-specked, clapboard shack." They came on in and wuz watchin me real close. Dere I wuz, the man they described as the "old Negro wearing layers of shirts, coats, socks and pants when it was 91 degrees outside."

Dey looked roun' and saw my "bare mattress stained by grime, smoke and sweat." I looked roun' and saw my life. My wife Hattie took good care of me and I luved her sumthin special.

We wuz happy, God-luving people and we had each otha'.

Da question dem kept askin; wuz how you livin' so long Uncle Odry? My answer wuz so simple it confused the lot of dem;

I ate from the creek and from my garden, I liked to keep movin, and I tried my best to 'njoy life wit my luved ones.

Wen you lose everythin', you figure out right quick wot's importan' and wots not. I ain't the smartest, but I got sense. I always do what the Bible tells me and try my best.

Yu got my sevin secrets but I got a hiddin one just fo yu. Mite say I saved the best one for las. Da real secret to long livin', ain't jus bout readin'... its bout what yur doin' and doin' on a regulah.

Do right, do yur best and stop worryin' bout living long.

Jus' live good.

All the so-called "secrets of success" will not work unless you do.

(ANONYMOUS)

Mr. Dalton and Ruby Randall (Lula Vaught's husband) carrying a crate of oysters to put in Mr. Dalton's truck.

YOUNGSTOWN VINDICATOR February 18, 1968

South Carolina Man, 123, Has Relatives Here

"When I saw him last summer he recognized me and called me by name," said Noble Bellamy, 94 Sixth St., Campbell, in talking about his 123-year-old great-uncle, Odrick Vaught in Myrtle Beach, S.C.

Vaught, who says he was 20 when John Wilkes Booth shot President Lincoln, recalls news stories of the tragedy. A feature and picture of Vaught was carried in a recent paper, "The State," in Columbia, S.C., saying that he is seriously ill in Ocean View Memorial Hospital in Myrtle Beach.

Bellamy's wife saw Vaught at Christmas time and said he recognized her, as well. Since that time he has become ill. He was born into slavery near Myrtle Beach and today may be the oldest living person in the United States. Bellamy, 60, formerly lived in Myrtle Beach and came to Campbell in 1925. He works at the Ohio Works of the U.S. Steel Corp.

ꙮ

Uncle O was missed by many, especially his dear friend Oliver Edge and the entire Moss family (his close neighbours).

Oliver Edge missing his dear friend Uncle O.

Isabelle Moss stands in Uncle O's doorway in search of something.

Lula Vaught (Odrick's niece) 75 years old, at water's edge behind Cherry Grove Beach, South Carolina.

Lula Vaught and Susan Bellamy, gathers large crates of oysters from the creek in Little River Neck, S.C.

Young James Melvin Moss missing Uncle O.

Melvin and Martha Lee Moss and children outside of Uncle Odrick's House in Little River Neck.

The Germination

The process of growing a new plant from a seed.

Uncle Odrick was a seed. He left behind an extraordinary legacy. His legacy was not built on riches or property. Uncle O handed down a legacy that was masterfully constructed based on one single trait, his character.

Follow his lead and germinate — one plant or one person, at a time.

Certificate of Achievement

OCT 4 1995

DIRECTOR

Registrar's No. 35

STATE OF SOUTH CAROLINA
BOARD OF HEALTH
CERTIFICATE OF DEATH

68-008280
STATE FILE NUMBER

Birth No.

1. DECEASED—NAME: MR. ODRICH VAUGHT
2. SEX: Male
3. DATE OF DEATH (MONTH, DAY, YEAR): 2-18-1968
4. RACE (WHITE, NEGRO, AMERICAN INDIAN, ETC.) (SPECIFY): Negro
5a. AGE—LAST BIRTHDAY (YEARS): 123
5b. UNDER 1 YEAR: MOS. DAYS
5c. UNDER 1 DAY: HOURS MIN.
6. DATE OF BIRTH (MONTH, DAY, YEAR): 1845
7a. COUNTY OF DEATH: Horry
7b. CITY, TOWN, OR LOCATION OF DEATH: Myrtle Beach
7c. INSIDE CITY LIMITS (SPECIFY YES OR NO): Yes
7d. HOSPITAL OR OTHER INSTITUTION—NAME (IF NOT IN EITHER, GIVE STREET AND NUMBER): OCEAN VIEW HOSPITAL, MYRTLE,BEACH, S. C.
8. STATE OF BIRTH (IF NOT IN U.S.A., NAME COUNTRY): S. C.
9. CITIZEN OF WHAT COUNTRY: U. S. A.
10. MARRIED, NEVER MARRIED, WIDOWED, DIVORCED (SPECIFY): Married
11. SURVIVING SPOUSE (IF WIFE, GIVE MAIDEN NAME): Mrs Hattie Vaught
12. SOCIAL SECURITY NUMBER: Unknown
13a. USUAL OCCUPATION (GIVE KIND OF WORK DONE DURING MOST OF WORKING LIFE, EVEN IF RETIRED): farm and fishing
13b. KIND OF BUSINESS OR INDUSTRY:
14a. RESIDENCE—STATE: S. C.
14b. COUNTY: Horry
14c. CITY, TOWN, OR LOCATION: Little River Neck,Sc
14d. INSIDE CITY LIMITS (SPECIFY YES OR NO): no
14e. STREET AND NUMBER: Rt. box 404,Ocean drive
15. FATHER—NAME: Jake Vaught
16. MOTHER—MAIDEN NAME:
17a. INFORMANT—NAME: Mrs Hattie Vaught
17b. MAILING ADDRESS (STREET OR R.F.D. NO., CITY OR TOWN, STATE, ZIP): Rt. 1 box 404, Ocean Drive, S. C. 29526

PART I. DEATH WAS CAUSED BY: (ENTER ONLY ONE CAUSE PER LINE FOR (a), (b), AND (c))

18. IMMEDIATE CAUSE
(a) Cerebral vascular accident — APPROXIMATE INTERVAL BETWEEN ONSET AND DEATH: 3-4 da
DUE TO, OR AS A CONSEQUENCE OF:
(b) ASCVD
DUE TO, OR AS A CONSEQUENCE OF:
(c)

CONDITIONS, IF ANY, WHICH GAVE RISE TO IMMEDIATE CAUSE (a), STATING THE UNDERLYING CAUSE LAST

PART II. OTHER SIGNIFICANT CONDITIONS: CONDITIONS CONTRIBUTING TO DEATH BUT NOT RELATED TO CAUSE GIVEN IN PART I (a): Unusually advanced age
19a. AUTOPSY (YES OR NO): no
19b. IF YES WERE FINDINGS CONSIDERED IN DETERMINING CAUSE OF DEATH

20a. ACCIDENT, SUICIDE, HOMICIDE, OR UNDETERMINED (SPECIFY)
20b. DATE OF INJURY (MONTH, DAY, YEAR)
20c. HOUR M.
20d. HOW INJURY OCCURRED (ENTER NATURE OF INJURY IN PART I OR PART II, ITEM 18)
20e. INJURY AT WORK (SPECIFY YES OR NO)
20f. PLACE OF INJURY AT HOME, FARM, STREET, FACTORY, OFFICE BLDG., ETC. (SPECIFY)
20g. LOCATION (STREET OR R.F.D. NO., CITY OR TOWN, STATE)

21a. CERTIFICATION— I ATTENDED THE DECEASED FROM: 2 7 68 TO 21b. 2 18 68
21c. AND LAST SAW HIM/HER ALIVE ON: 2 18 68
21d. I DID/DID NOT VIEW THE BODY AFTER DEATH: did
21e. DEATH OCCURRED (HOUR): 12:10 P M. AT THE PLACE, ON THE DATE, AND, TO THE BEST OF MY KNOWLEDGE, DUE TO THE CAUSE(S) STATED
22a. CERTIFIER—NAME: DONALD L. DUERK, M. D.
22b. SIGNATURE: Donald L. Duerk MD — DEGREE OR TITLE
22c. DATE SIGNED (MONTH, DAY, YEAR): 3/8/68
22d. MAILING ADDRESS—CERTIFIER: HWY N. MYRTLE BEACH, S. C. 29577
23a. BURIAL, CREMATION, REMOVAL (SPECIFY): Burial
23b. CEMETERY OR CREMATORY—NAME: St. Paul Cemetery
23c. LOCATION: Ocean Drive, Horry, S. C.
23d. DATE (MONTH, DAY, YEAR): 2-22-1968
24a. FUNERAL HOME—NAME AND ADDRESS (STREET OR R.F.D. NO., CITY OR TOWN, STATE, ZIP): McKievers Funeral Home, Conway, S. C.
24b. FUNERAL DIRECTOR—SIGNATURE: George L. Williams Jr.
25a. REGISTRAR—SIGNATURE: Mrs. Emily C. Bennett
25b. DATE RECEIVED BY LOCAL REGISTRAR: March 15,1968

Don't worry 'bout a thing.